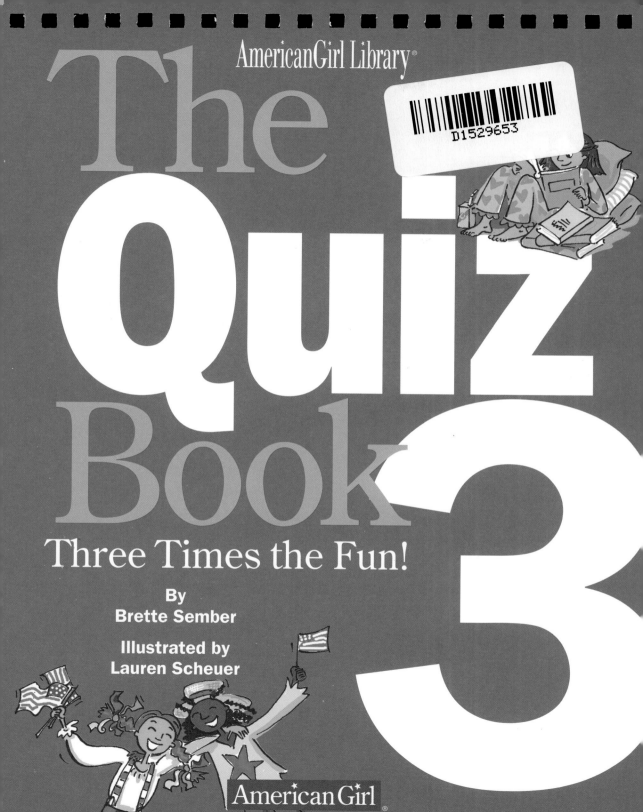

American Girl Library®

The Quiz Book 3

Three Times the Fun!

By
Brette Sember

Illustrated by
Lauren Scheuer

American Girl®

Dear Reader,

You asked for it! You begged for it! And now it's here—
Quiz Book 3 with **26** all-new, fun quizzes to help you
learn even more about you.

What kind of friend are you? How do you spend your
free time? Are you **stressed out?** Do you hold a
grudge? Your answers to the questions in this book
will reveal more about the true you!

You'll also find quizzes that help you see how much you
know about your **friends and family** and about yourself
when you were little. When you're done, quiz a friend,
quiz **your sister,** quiz everyone you know . . . and
then, quiz yourself again and again!

Until next time—

Your friends at American Girl

Contents

Hue Do You Do?

Your **favorite color** reveals a lot about you. Circle your fave-colored tee, then turn the page to see how it colors your personality.

☐ **Red**

☐ Yellow

☐ **Blue**

☐ Green

☐ Orange

☐ **Black**

☐ White

☐ **Brown**

☐ **Purple**

☐ Pink

Answers

Red: If you love red, you're all about excitement. You love to be at the center of the action. Your feelings can be very intense.

Yellow: You are carefree. You always look on the bright side of things. You also love to feel warm and cozy.

Blue: You tend to appreciate some time alone, but you can be a really loyal friend. You are very organized.

Green: You're full of energy and ready to try new things. You also like to look on the bright side of things.

Orange: You're pretty satisfied with your life. You like to get things accomplished and often try to do good deeds.

Black: You are serious, and you make a good leader. You like to be in charge and organize things.

White: You're very honest, and you try to do things the right way. You like to keep your things neat and clean.

Brown: You think that when you get right down to it, you're a pretty decent person. People can count on you, and you make a very dependable friend.

Purple: You are creative and witty. You love to fantasize. In your dreams, you are a princess!

Pink: You have a very calm personality. Your feelings are very important to you and can be easily hurt. You love to daydream.

Rock Around the Clock

Are you **bright-eyed in the morning, nifty in the afternoon,** or a **night creature?**

To find out, pick the answer that fits you best.

1. If it were up to you, you would automatically wake up at . . .

a. 7 A.M. You've got things to do, people to see, and places to go!

b. 8:30 A.M. What's the hurry?

C. 10 A.M. A growing girl needs her sleep, you know!

2. Be it a cute cat sitting in a neighbor's window or a funny joke someone tells you, you are most likely to remember details about . . .

a. your trip to school in the morning.

b. your trip home from school in the afternoon.

C. your bike ride after dinner.

3. You have a big math test on Friday. You've studied and you're ready to ace the test, but you would do best if it were scheduled for . . .

a. first period—bright and early while your brain is fresh.

b. fifth period—right after you fill up on brain food.

C. last period—when your brain is really humming along.

4. Yakety-yak. You're most likely to chat up a storm . . .

   a. first thing in the morning when you see your friends at school.

   b. hanging out after school.

   c. at the dinner table or on the phone before bedtime.

5. At a slumber party, you're usually . . .

   a. the first to crash.

   b. dozing off right about the same time as the other guests.

   c. the last one to fall asleep.

6. Everyone gets a little grumpy now and then. For you, it happens mostly . . .

   a. at night before bedtime.

   b. Who, me? Grumpy?

   c. in the early morning after waking up.

7. To make sure you have lots of energy, you schedule your tennis lessons on Saturdays during the . . .

   a. morning.

   b. afternoon.

   c. evening.

8. You have to memorize and recite the poem "Where the Sidewalk Ends" for English class next week, so you practice . . .

a. every morning—things sink in better then.

b. after school, when you're plowing through the rest of your homework.

c. in the evening, because you can concentrate best then.

9. All good things must come to an end. When it's not a school night, you hit the sack at . . .

a. 9 P.M.—like clockwork!

b. 10 P.M.—after all the good shows on TV are over.

c. 11 P.M.—zonked out with the light on is more like it.

Answers

Mostly a's

Morning Mover

Even if you're not always up before the rooster crows, mornings are when you're at your perkiest.

Mostly b's

Afternoon Ace

It takes you a while to warm up and get into the day. Afternoons are when you're at your best.

Mostly C's

Night Owl

The moon and the stars are your brightest lights. You're not fully in gear until evening falls.

Baby Talk

How much do you know about **yourself as a baby?**
Answer the questions and get a parent to correct them for you.

1. Day of the week you were born ....

2. Your first word ....

3. Time of day you were born ....

4. How old you were when you crawled ....

5. How old you were when you walked ....

6. What your name would have been if you'd been a boy ....

7. Whether you were born early, late, or on time ....

8. Name of hospital or place where you were born ....

9. Your favorite baby toy ....

10. How old you were when you got your first tooth ....

11. Why your parents picked your name ....

12. Where your parents lived when you were a baby ....

13. What color your hair was when you were born ....

14. Your favorite way to be put to sleep ....

15. The color of your baby blanket ....

16. Your favorite lullaby ....

17. Whether you were a good sleeper, an O.K. sleeper, or awake all night

every night ....

18. Your favorite baby food ....

19. How much you weighed at birth ....

20. How long you were at birth ....

Scoring

Give yourself **1 point** for each correct answer.

15 to 20 points
History Buff

You know a lot about your early years. You must have read that baby memory book and enjoyed a lot of "When you were a baby . . ." stories.

8 to 14 points
Goo-Goo Good

You already have many of the facts about your beginnings. There are probably some stories you haven't heard, though. Find out what else your parents or relatives can tell you about you!

0 to 7 points
Ba-Ba Baffled!

There's so much to learn about your babyhood. Go through the questions with your parents and ask them to help you learn more about sweet little you!

Sweet Dreams

Some are scary and some are silly, but your **dreams** have meanings.
Match what you may dream about with what it might mean.

___ **1.** Being hugged

___ **2.** Falling

___ **3.** A car

___ **4.** Flying

___ **5.** A tornado

___ **6.** Being lost or trapped

___ **7.** An animal

___ **8.** Being naked in public

___ **9.** Being chased

___ **10.** Being late for school or not ready for a test

___ **11.** A house

a. You're afraid of something.

b. You're nervous.

c. This symbol represents you.

d. You feel good or confident about something.

e. This symbol stands for part of your personality.

f. You feel anxious or unprepared.

g. You don't feel in control.

h. You feel exposed or vulnerable.

i. You want to be closer to a person.

j. You're confused.

k. What happens with this symbol stands for what's happening with you.

13

Answers

1. Being hugged, i. When you dream about hugging, it means you want to be closer to the person you are hugging or you want to be more like him or her.

2. Falling, b. If you dream you're falling, you probably feel nervous about something in your life—for example, a science project that you can't seem to get finished.

3. Car, k. What is happening with a car in your dream stands for something happening with you. For example, if the car is going in a new direction, you might be trying some new things or meeting new people.

4. Flying, d. Flying means you feel good or confident about something. This kind of dream can also mean you feel free.

5. Tornado, g. A dream about a tornado symbolizes that you feel lack of control over something in your life. You might be under too much pressure or going through something emotional like a big change.

6. Being lost or trapped, j. A dream in which you're lost or trapped means you're feeling confused about something in your life, such as an argument you and your best friend had.

7. Animal, e. Animals that you dream about stand for parts of your personality. Think about the animal in the dream and how you are like it. A dream about an ostrich might be about your shy side, while a dream about a graceful swan might be about your dancing ability.

8. Being naked in public, h. This kind of dream means you feel exposed or vulnerable about something. For example, maybe you're worried about forgetting your lines in the school play.

9. Being chased, a. Dreams where you're being chased mean that there is something in your life you are afraid of, such as a big test, moving to a new town, or a parent losing a job. Your dream might be giving your mind a chance to face the fear and find the courage to get through it.

10. Being late for school/not ready for a test, f. This kind of dream means you feel unprepared for something or you are anxious about something. Try making a list of what you need to do before going to bed to ease your mind.

11. House, c. Dreams about houses or rooms in houses are really about you. The room you dream about represents a part of your life. A house dream might mean you're thinking carefully about something that you're not so sure about.

Do You Want to Be a Millionaire?

What would **you** do for a million dollars?

1. Give up the computer forever.

_____ **No problem** _____ No way!

2. Eat deep-fried octopus dipped in hot sauce.

_____ **No problem** _____ No way!

3. Share your room with a three-year-old for a year.

_____ **No problem** _____ No way!

4. Get a tattoo that says, "Boys are smarter than girls."

_____ **No problem** _____ No way!

5. Cook dinner every night for six months.

_____ **No problem** _____ No way!

6. Stick your arm into a swarming beehive.

_____ **No problem** _____ No way!

15

7. Walk to the North Pole.

_____ No problem _____ No way!

8. Drink goat's milk.

_____ No problem _____ No way!

9. Listen only to opera music for the next ten years.

_____ No problem _____ No way!

10. Go bungee jumping.

_____ No problem _____ No way!

11. Walk barefoot through a ditch filled with big, slimy slugs.

_____ No problem _____ No way!

12. Not talk to your best friend for three months.

_____ No problem _____ No way!

13. Tap dance to "Yankee Doodle Dandy" in front of the whole school, wearing an orange sequined leotard and green polka-dot tights.

_____ No problem _____ No way!

14. Hang glide over an active volcano.

_____ No problem _____ No way!

15. Chew a piece of bubble gum that was stuck to the bottom of someone's shoe.

_____ No problem _____ No way!

16. Publish your diary in the newspaper.

_____ No problem _____ No way!

17. Let your parents pick out your clothes for the rest of your life.

_____ No problem _____ No way!

Scoring

1 or more "No problem"s

Congratulations! You got the cash. But was it worth it? Do you know where that bubble gum has been?

0 "No problem"s

Your good sense is priceless! Is there ANYTHING you'd do for a million bucks? Now, that's a million-dollar question!

Predict Your Friend's Future

Get out your crystal ball and **look into the future.** Where will your best bud be? What will she do? How will she live? Guess your friend's hopes and dreams, then have her check your answers.

1. Your friend's dream home is . . .

a. a loft apartment in a big city.

b. a house with a white picket fence and a big yard.

c. a motor home, cruising from spot to spot.

2. After she graduates from high school, she would like to . . .

a. travel overseas.

b. start a rock band.

c. hit the books in college.

d. marry her high-school sweetheart.

e. train for the Olympics.

18

3. She would love a job as . . .

a. a lawyer standing up for people's rights.

b. a gourmet chef with a chain of 4-star restaurants, a cooking show, and her own brand of spaghetti sauce.

c. a greeting card illustrator who cares to draw the very best.

d. an investigative reporter who searches relentlessly for the truth.

e. a psychic advisor to the nation's president.

f. a wildlife expert who specializes in protecting endangered manatees.

4. Her house will have . . .

a. lots of animal prints, candles, and fountains.

b. plenty of lace, pillows, and flowers.

c. movable walls, a retractable roof, videophones, and all kinds of other high-tech gadgets.

d. just the basics—she would spend her money on other things.

5. When you look in her fridge, you'll find . . .

a. an empty pizza box and a jar of mayo.

b. sushi, taco fixin's, take-out Chinese, and other ethnic foods.

c. nothing but veggies.

d. 33 flavors of ice cream.

6. As a grown-up, she'll live . . .

    a. with her husband and kids.

    b. with a collection of pets.

    c. with some nutty roommates.

    d. by herself—and love it!

    e. on the road, seeing the country.

7. Her favorite hangout will be . . .

    a. a trendy corner coffee shop.

    b. a noisy soccer field.

    c. the beach at sunset.

    d. her own backyard.

    e. a funky art museum.

8. Her big, big dream is to . . .

    a. record a top-ten smash hit.

    b. find a cure for a terrible disease.

    c. backpack through the Himalayas.

    d. win the lottery.

    e. just be happy.

9. Her first set of wheels will be a . . .

a. big red pickup truck.

b. racy red convertible.

c. cute green VW bug.

d. mountain bike.

e. new electric car that doesn't guzzle gas.

10. On her 21st birthday, she will . . .

a. catch a shuttle to the moon to celebrate.

b. have cake and ice cream with family and friends.

c. plan a Big Birthday Blowout Bash and invite 100 of her closest friends.

d. tell everyone not to make a fuss but then be surprised with a party.

Scoring
Give yourself **1 point** for each correct answer.

0 to 3 points
Unknown Quantity
Your friend has dreams and plans you never knew about. Take some time to discuss the wishes and hopes both of you have for the future.

4 to 7 points
Friends for Sure
You're clued in to what she wants. Does she know what you dream about? Have her take the quiz now!

8 to 10 points
Mind Reader
Put down that crystal ball! You really know your pal well. Try the quiz with another friend and see how well you do.

Do You Mope or Cope?

When things don't go your way, how do you react? Choose the answer that fits you best in each situation, and find out about **your coping style.** Be honest . . .

1. Your grade on the science test was not as good as you had hoped. You're mad at yourself for blowing it and worry about the bad grade for the rest of the day.

☐ That's me.

☐ No way—I would just stick the test in my folder and decide to study more next time.

2. You desperately wanted to win that fluffy stuffed puppy at the carnival, but you just couldn't get it and your whole day is ruined.

☐ That's me.

☐ Not me—I would focus on playing other games and munching on funnel cakes and cotton candy.

3. Your gerbil got loose and you can't find him anywhere. You can't stop blaming yourself for leaving your door open and bury your head in your pillow, worrying about all the bad things that could happen to him.

☐ That's me.

☐ No time for that—I would beg forgiveness and ask my parents to help me find that little guy.

4. You finished your homework just in time to watch your favorite TV show. Only problem? A storm knocked out the power just as the show was about to start. You sit on the couch moaning about what you're missing.

☐ That's me.

☐ No way! I would have fun playing games by candlelight with my family, and I'd catch the show on the reruns.

5. You tried out for the school play but found out today that you didn't make it. You shut yourself in your bedroom and decide that your acting career is over . . . finished . . . kaput!

☐ That's me.

☐ Not this girl. I might feel sad for a little while, but I would keep practicing hard and try out again next year.

6. You're finishing the cover for your book report. It's getting late, but you really hate the way your drawing looks. You crumple the page and throw the whole thing out. No way can you turn it in like that.

☐ That's me.

☐ Not quite. I would take a break, have a snack, walk the dog, and then come back to it. It's not THAT bad.

Scoring

4 or more
"That's me" answers:

Mope Mode. You tend to let things get you down. Try looking for solutions instead of letting yourself focus on the bad side of things.

3 or fewer
"That's me" answers:

Mope? Nope! You like to face a tough situation head on and do something about it. You take things as they come and make the best of whatever happens.

Ways to cope with what gets you down:

● **Take a break.** Sometimes when you come back to a problem, it doesn't seem nearly as bad as it did when you first discovered it.

● **Make a plan.** Solving a problem can be less overwhelming when it's broken into smaller tasks.

● **Ask for help.** Sometimes you need a parent, teacher, or other grown-up to help you solve a particular problem.

● **Take a deep breath.** Think to yourself, *What's the worst that can happen here?* Chances are, it's not as bad as you first thought. Write down five things that you can do to improve your situation. Then, do them!

Eyewitness

Try this test of your attention to detail. Otis the puppy got into your room. He messed everything up, and now **five things are missing.** Can you tell what they are?

Before Otis

Look at this picture for one minute.

Tick, tick, tick . . . ding! Time's up! Now put the book down and do something else for one minute.
Braid your hair, count your freckles—whatever. But make sure you wait at least a minute.
Now look at the next page.

List what's missing:

1. _____ 2. _____ 3. _____

4. _____ 5. _____

Hold this page up to a mirror to see the answers revealed below.

How'd you do?

Scoring

1 or none right	2 or 3 right	4 or 5 right
Clueless	Looking Good	Ace Detective!

Answers: math notebook, teddy bear, baseball cap, bunny slipper, baseball

Mall Madness

It's time to play Mall Madness! Find out **what kind of shopper** you are by working your way through the splendiferous stores ahead. On your mark, get set, SHOP!

1. Your mom just bought you a pair of new sneakers yesterday, but there in the shoe department is a pair of the most fabulous sneakers. They're in your size and they're on sale. You . . .

   a. grab them and make a beeline for the register.

   b. touch them lightly, wince, then go home and put on the ones your mom bought you.

2. The new CD from your favorite group just came out today. The music store has only one copy left. Your wallet is empty. You . . .

   a. promise your mom that if she buys it for you, you'll take out the trash without needing to be reminded.

   b. give it a good once-over but put it back. Maybe you'll hear the songs on the radio before Mom gives you your next allowance.

3. While browsing in the bookstore, you discover that the next issue of your favorite magazine is out—and Joey Allen Poe is on the cover! You . . .

   a. snag it—you just can't wait to read this one!

   b. wait to read your best friend's copy, because she has a subscription.

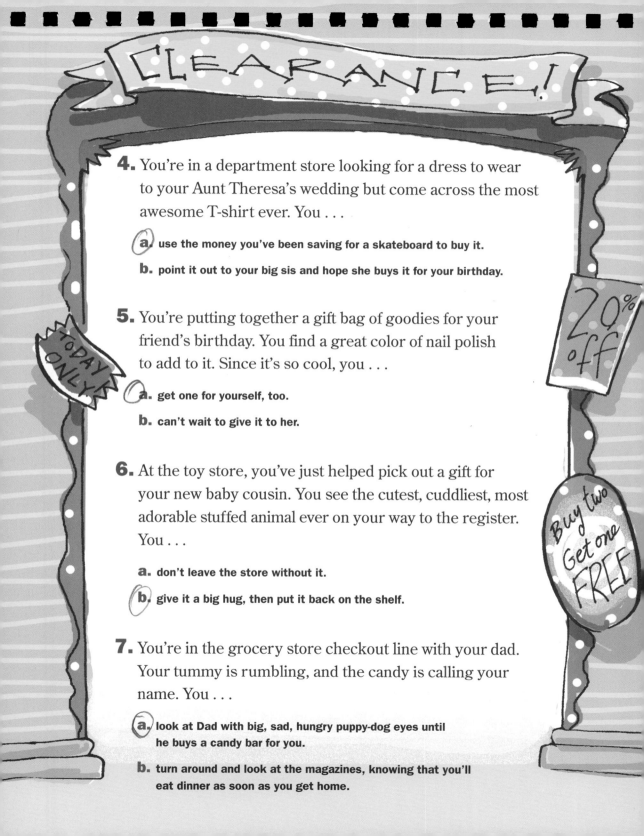

4. You're in a department store looking for a dress to wear to your Aunt Theresa's wedding but come across the most awesome T-shirt ever. You . . .

a. use the money you've been saving for a skateboard to buy it.

b. point it out to your big sis and hope she buys it for your birthday.

5. You're putting together a gift bag of goodies for your friend's birthday. You find a great color of nail polish to add to it. Since it's so cool, you . . .

a. get one for yourself, too.

b. can't wait to give it to her.

6. At the toy store, you've just helped pick out a gift for your new baby cousin. You see the cutest, cuddliest, most adorable stuffed animal ever on your way to the register. You . . .

a. don't leave the store without it.

b. give it a big hug, then put it back on the shelf.

7. You're in the grocery store checkout line with your dad. Your tummy is rumbling, and the candy is calling your name. You . . .

a. look at Dad with big, sad, hungry puppy-dog eyes until he buys a candy bar for you.

b. turn around and look at the magazines, knowing that you'll eat dinner as soon as you get home.

TODAY ONLY!

20% off

Buy two Get one FREE

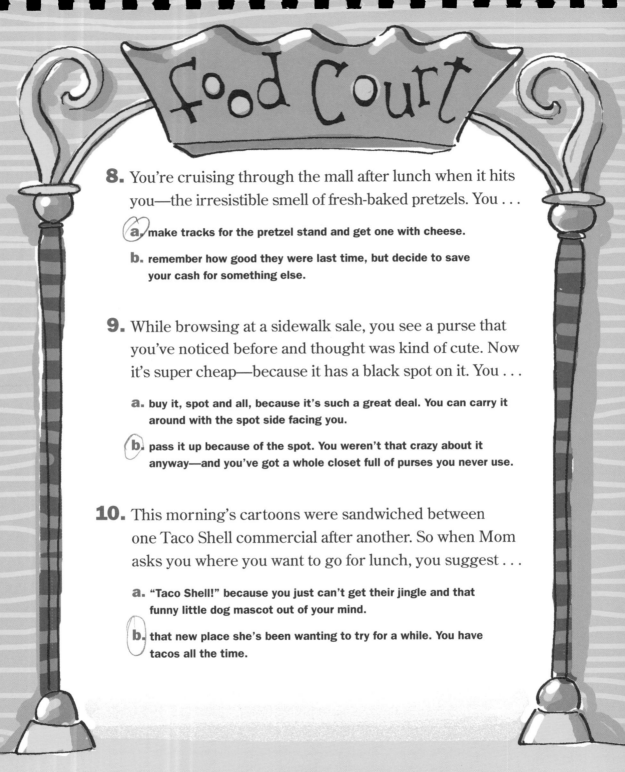

food court

8. You're cruising through the mall after lunch when it hits you—the irresistible smell of fresh-baked pretzels. You . . .

a. make tracks for the pretzel stand and get one with cheese.

b. remember how good they were last time, but decide to save your cash for something else.

9. While browsing at a sidewalk sale, you see a purse that you've noticed before and thought was kind of cute. Now it's super cheap—because it has a black spot on it. You . . .

a. buy it, spot and all, because it's such a great deal. You can carry it around with the spot side facing you.

b. pass it up because of the spot. You weren't that crazy about it anyway—and you've got a whole closet full of purses you never use.

10. This morning's cartoons were sandwiched between one Taco Shell commercial after another. So when Mom asks you where you want to go for lunch, you suggest . . .

a. "Taco Shell!" because you just can't get their jingle and that funny little dog mascot out of your mind.

b. that new place she's been wanting to try for a while. You have tacos all the time.

Answers

Mostly a's

"Gotta Have It" Gal

You love to buy on impulse. It's fun to spend, spend, spend, but sometimes it's better to take a step back and think it over before coughing up the cash. Next time you're about to ring up another sale, ask yourself some questions: "Do I really need this?" "What could I save for instead of buying this?" In other words, "Am I just buying this because of advertising or a super low price?"

Mostly b's

Thoughtful Spender

You're careful with your dough, and you're good at not letting emotions drain your wallet. Kudos to you for taking the time to think about what you want versus what you need—and for not being swayed by ploys used by companies trying to sell things to you.

Happily Ever After?

It's your turn to tell the tale! Choose new endings to these fairy tales and find out **how you like to solve problems.**

1. When the three bears returned home, they should have . . .

   a. called 9-1-1—there was a stranger in the house!

   b. had a beauty party where they made Goldilocks a redhead.

2. Cinderella should have . . .

   a. asked the fairy godmother to change the stepsisters into nice people.

   b. kicked off the glass slippers, ordered a pizza, and invited the prince and the godmother for a late-night snack.

3. If you wrote the story, Hansel and Gretel would have . . .

   a. brought trail mix and a cell phone along in case they got lost.

   b. turned the witch into a gingerbread cookie and eaten her!

4. Snow White would have been better off if she . . .

   a. had tossed the poison apple and kept on cleaning house.

   b. had gone on tour singing "Heigh-ho, Heigh-ho, It's Home from Work We Go," with the dwarves as backup and the prince as her manager.

5. "Little Red Riding Hood" should have ended with . . .

   a. Red Riding Hood convincing the wolf to cut it out and have some tea and muffins with her and Grandmother.

   b. Red Riding Hood overpowering the wolf. Those Tae Kwon Do lessons paid off!

6. "The Three Little Pigs" would have been a better story if . . .

   a. the three little pigs had convinced the wolf to become a vegetarian.

   b. the pigs' houses had secret underground tunnels through which they escaped to a space shuttle that took them to their REAL home on the moon.

7. "Jack and the Beanstalk" should have ended with . . .

a. Jack and the giant agreeing to share the goose.

b. Jack and his mother opening the Beanstalk Amusement Park, featuring the Golden Goose Log Flume, the Tickle-the-Giant Sideshow, and the Magic Beans Super Slide.

8. Rapunzel should have . . .

a. offered to make the witch a wig out of some of her hair in exchange for being set free.

b. parachuted out of the tower and gone straight to the hairstylist for a snazzy new 'do.

Answers

Mostly a's
A Lot o' Logic

You use logic and rational problem solving to get yourself out of jams (and to keep from getting into them!). You think before you act, always have a plan, and need to know the reason behind something before buying into it.

Mostly b's
A Bit o' Whimsy

You have quite an imagination! You're creative and fun in your problem solving. You always look for new, different answers. You like to see happy endings, but you're also up for exciting twists and turns along the way.

Raise Your Hand

Some people believe that **palm reading,** or looking at the lines on your hands, can tell you about your personality. Look at your palms and the information on the next page and see if you agree!

Heart line

Head line

Life line

Head Line

Your head line tells what kind of thinker you are. If it's straight, you are logical and interested in facts. If it curves down a bit, you are good at math and science. If it curves down a lot, you're very creative and imaginative.

Heart Line

Your heart line tells about your feelings. The stronger the heart line, the more affectionate and caring you may be. If it slants up, you are a true, warmhearted friend. If it's straight, your head rules your heart.

Use the guide on page 33 and draw your lines here.

Life Line

Your life line tells you how much energy you have, not how long you'll live. The stronger and clearer it is, the more energetic you are.

34

Back in the Day

What were your parents like at your age? What did they consider cool, neat, or cute? Write the answers to the following questions with one parent in mind. Then have mom or dad check your answers to find out how much you know.

1. Street he or she grew up on ....

2. Pet's name ....

3. Best friend's name ....

4. Favorite relative ....

5. Name of school attended ....

6. Best school subject ....

7. Favorite hangout ....

8. Dream job ....

9. Subject of posters on bedroom wall ....

10. Best gift ever ....

11. Favorite book ....

12. Favorite Halloween costume ....

13. Favorite toy or belonging ....

14. Favorite TV show ....

15. Number of televisions in the house ....

16. Favorite movie star ....

17. Favorite band or singer ....

18. Kept a collection of ....

19. Favorite board game ....

20. Favorite sport ....

21. Favorite team ....

22. Favorite drink ....

23. Favorite fast food ....

24. Favorite sweet treat ....

25. Least favorite veggie ....

26. Favorite holiday ....

27. Family vacation spot ....

28. Price of a school lunch ....

29. Amount of allowance ....

30. President of the United States ....

Scoring

Give yourself 1 point for each correct answer.

0 to 9 points

Things were really different when your parent was a kid! There's so much to learn about life back then and about what your parent was like. Go through the quiz together and learn more!

10 to 19 points

Although you know quite a bit about what your parent did as a kid, there's more to learn and probably quite a few funny stories you haven't heard. Have your parent tell you the answers you missed!

20 to 30 points

Wow! You must have listened carefully to those "When I was your age . . ." stories. You know a lot about your parent's life as a kid. Try taking the quiz with another parent or relative in mind.

Doyouknowthis.com

Are you up on the latest **Internet I.M. lingo?**
Log on to this quiz, enter your answers in the blanks,
then scroll to the next page to check them.

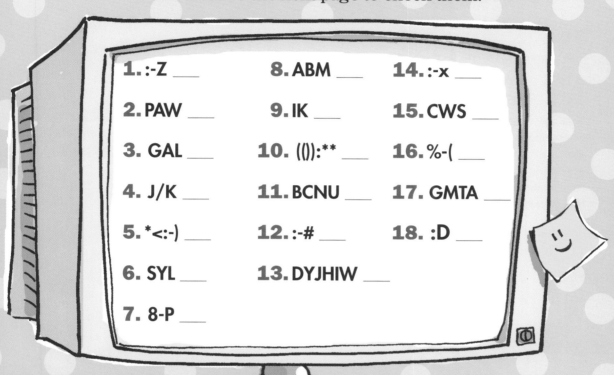

1. :-Z ___
2. PAW ___
3. GAL ___
4. J/K ___
5. *<:-) ___
6. SYL ___
7. 8-P ___
8. ABM ___
9. IK ___
10. (()):** ___
11. BCNU ___
12. :-# ___
13. DYJHIW ___
14. :-x ___
15. CWS ___
16. %-(___
17. GMTA ___
18. :D ___

a. Just kidding
b. Santa Claus
c. Parents are watching
d. Cool Web stuff
e. I know
f. See ya later
g. Get a life
h. Be seeing you
i. Yuck
j. Sleeping
k. Great minds think alike
l. A big mistake
m. Confused
n. Don't you just hate it when
o. Hugs and kisses
p. Keeping lips sealed
q. Someone with braces
r. Laughing

Answers

1. j. Sleeping **2. c.** Parents are watching **3. g.** Get a life **4. a.** Just kidding **5. b.** Santa Claus **6. f.** See ya later **7. i.** Yuck **8. l.** A big mistake **9. e.** I know **10. o.** Hugs and kisses **11. h.** Be seeing you **12. q.** Someone with braces **13. n.** Don't you just hate it when **14. p.** Keeping lips sealed **15. d.** Cool Web stuff **16. m.** Confused **17. k.** Great minds think alike **18. r.** Laughing

Scoring

Give yourself **1 point** for each correct answer.

0 to 6 points
In Training
Need a little practice in e-conversations? Give a few of these abbreviations and emoticons a try. (If you don't have a computer at home, test-drive one at your local library.)

7 to 12 points
With It
You're pretty hip when it comes to knowing Internet talk. Try making up more codes of your own!

13 to 18 points
It Clicked!
You're a computer queen. You've probably even made up a few of your own abbreviations and emoticons!

40

What Kind of Friend Are You?

Are you the **first one to give a hug, always ready to rescue,** or **not so sure** where you stand?
Take this quiz to find out!

1. Your friend Neeta is thinking about signing up for the science-fair competition at school. You . . .

❑ tell Neeta that it's a great idea! Then tell her you can do the project together and start sketching your plans.

❑ wonder if you should sign up, too. You don't want to miss anything . . . but you aren't really sure either.

☑ **are so excited for her, you make plans to attend and show your support.**

2. Yikes! Your teacher surprised everyone with a pop quiz in social studies today. Afterward, you say to your friends . . .

☑ **"No one was really prepared, but I bet we all did O.K." Then you put your arms around them and make a run for the monkey bars.**

❑ "How many do you think you got wrong?"

❑ "Let's study together this weekend so we're prepared next time."

3. Kristen is wearing a new fuzzy sweater that everyone totally loves. Your reaction is to . . .

☑ tell her how great it looks on her.

☐ zip your coat so no one looks next at the plain old sweatshirt you're wearing.

☐ ask her where she got it and have your mom buy you the exact same one.

4. Your soccer team makes it to the finals but loses in the last minute of the game. After the game, you . . .

☑ congratulate your teammates on a terrific season and remind them that there's always next year.

☐ tell everyone that you're going to organize an off-season conditioning program.

☐ worry that your teammates think it was your fault you lost—you should have made that goal you missed.

5. Valerie tells you her parents are getting divorced and she has to move away. You . . .

☑ tell her you're sorry and you'll always be her friend whenever she needs to talk.

☐ worry that you'll never make another friend.

☐ start planning a going-away party and think of ways you can e-mail and visit each other.

6. Jen comes to school on crutches after she sprained her ankle. You . . .

☐ secretly wish you were the one on crutches so that you could get all the attention.

☑ ask her how it happened and tell her how sorry you are that she got hurt.

☐ carry her books for her and put your sweatshirt under her foot to elevate it.

7. Lily has been your best friend since first grade, but lately she doesn't sit next to you during lunch and seems to want to hang out only with Laura. You . . .

☐ make sure that Lily is on your committee to decorate the gym for the dance . . . and Laura *isn't.*

☑ sneak a note into her locker telling her that you miss her.

☐ can't help but wonder why she doesn't like you anymore.

8. It's the last day of school! The last thing you do at school is . . .

☑ give all your friends big hugs.

☐ peek over your friends' shoulders as they open their report cards.

☐ make sure all your friends have each others' camp addresses for care packages!

Answers

mostly blue

You are always ready to lend an ear and offer words of encouragement to your friends. You know yourself and you know how to be a good friend at the same time. Your friends can count on you.

mostly red

You are creative—a natural leader! You like to plan, coordinate, and help out. But you need to be careful not to take too much control, especially when no one asks you to. Be patient, listen, and try not to always jump to the rescue! You might find some ways to put your leadership skills to use, like heading up the school food drive.

mostly yellow

You sometimes feel insecure about yourself. Try to remember that you, too, have special strengths, and don't put so much emphasis on how you measure up to your pals.

Boy Barometer

Are boys your **new hobby, just O.K.,** or **pretty icky?**
Check the barometer and see what your reading is.

1. You have new assigned seats in math class, and you're stuck between two boys. You . . .

   a. don't know how you will live through it.

   b. don't really mind because they are nice enough guys.

   c. think it's pretty cool.

2. Your friend Jade likes Dominic, and she won't stop talking about him. You . . .

   a. think she's nuts.

   b. aren't sure why she wants to gush but are O.K. listening to the details . . . for a little while.

   c. ask Jade if Dominic has any friends.

3. You sign up for a summer class in archery but find out you're the only girl in the class. You . . .

   a. drop out and take swimming instead.

   b. go because you really want to do this.

   c. can hardly wait—being the only girl will be so cool!

45

4. Your gym teacher announces that the boys and girls will be together outside today for track. Your first thought is . . .

   a. "My stomach hurts. I'm going to the nurse's office."

   b. "I love the long jump."

   c. "I'm going to need extra time to look just right for this."

5. You're invited to your friend Kevin's birthday party. The first thing you do is . . .

   a. throw out the invitation. You don't want people to think you like him.

   b. call to RSVP. He's a friend, so of course you'll go.

   c. call your friends to tell them you're going to a girl-boy birthday party.

6. Jay is the only person your age at the family holiday party for your mom's office. You . . .

   a. ignore him and go help out at the beanbag toss for the little kids.

   b. roll your eyes at him when someone suggests you dance together.

   c. trade seats with someone so that you end up sitting next to him for the dinner.

7. You're staying at your aunt's house. You're looking for a book to read, but all you find are your cousin's teen fan magazines. You . . .

   a. forget about reading and go see if she has cable.

   b. read a little of one that has your favorite actor on the front.

   c. stack them up and plan to read every single one before you leave.

8. Student Council has planned an end-of-year dance for your grade. You . . .

a. would rather invite some friends over to play board games at your house that night.

b. plan to go, but only if you and your best bud can go together.

c. hope that the cute guy who just moved here will ask you to go with him.

Scoring

Give yourself 0 points for each **a**, 1 point for each **b**, and 2 points for each **c**. Color in one of the sections on the barometer for each point.

0 to 4
No Thanks
Chances are you have better things to do than worry about boys. It is perfectly fine not to be gaga over guys. Go with what makes you feel comfortable.

5 to 9
Boy Friends?
For you, boys don't have to be "boyfriends." You are able to get to know boys for who they are and even enjoy being friends with some of them.

10 to 16
Oh Boy!
It's nice to be friendly and even curious about boys, but ask yourself if your new hobby is taking over your life. Boys are just . . . boys. Keep your other interests alive, too.

47

Singing Sensation

Are you cut out to be **a diva, a songwriter,** or **a manager to the stars?** Find out where you fit in the entertainment biz. Check each statement that applies to you.

_____ I love being in front of a crowd.

_____ I'm very good at organizing.

_____ I always have lots of exciting new ideas.

_____ I'm happiest when I'm alone.

_____ People look to me to make decisions.

_____ I adore flashy new fashions.

_____ I sometimes exaggerate.

_____ I like to plan things out.

_____ I keep a journal or sketchbook.

_____ I adore it when people pay attention to me.

_____ I like to be near excitement but not right in the middle of it.

48

_____ I am usually pretty quiet, but there's a lot going on inside my head.

_____ I am proud of my abilities, and I am not afraid to stand up and show the world what I can do.

_____ Music, art, and poetry make life worthwhile.

_____ I try not to get caught up in silly things and try to keep myself focused.

Answers

Mostly red

Delightful Diva
You love to be the star of the show and would be at home at center stage.

Mostly blue

Management Material
You love to organize and be a leader. You would do a great job steering a star's career.

Mostly green

Certainly a Songwriter
You tend to be creative and are happiest when you can give your free spirit room to play.

Read Between the Lines

What kind of books get you hooked?
Check out this quiz and find your **book style.**

1. You and a pal decide to go see a movie. You've just got to see the one called . . .

   a. *Spy Twins.*

   b. *Behind the Velvet Curtains: Secrets of Teenage Royalty.*

   c. *Pandas in China: A Rescue Mission.*

2. You're in the grocery checkout line with your dad. Which headline catches your eye?

   a. "Aliens Have Arrived" on the front page of the *American Inquirer*

   b. "101 Great Ideas for Girls' Bedrooms" in *Beautiful Home*

   c. "Kids Care: Volunteer Opportunities for Kids" in the *Everyday News*

3. Your computer user name is . . .

   a. a secret.

   b. Dreamer.

   c. Down-2-Earth.

4. You're shipwrecked on a desert island. You plan to . . .

   a. learn to spearfish and track the large paw prints you've seen in the sand.

   b. use coconuts and shells to create a rocket that will hone in on the nearest aircraft carrier and alert the crew to your location.

   c. keep a daily journal—once you're rescued, you'll sell your life story.

5. Your favorite board game is . . .

   a. Clue.

   b. The Game of Life.

   c. Trivial Pursuit.

6. When you were little, you liked to play . . .

   a. Hide-and-Seek.

   b. Dress-Up.

   c. House.

7. The creatures that interest you the most are . . .

a. the Loch Ness Monster and Bigfoot.

b. unicorns and trolls.

c. dogs and horses.

8. It's time to plan your family's summer vacation. You suggest . . .

a. a Secret Escape—a travel agent makes all the arrangements, and nobody knows where you're headed until a few days before the trip.

b. a Caribbean cruise—just like in the movies!

c. a family reunion—what a perfect way to meet all your cousins.

9. On your birthday, the gift you want to open first is . . .

a. the giant box that makes a strange noise when you shake it.

b. the one wrapped in shiny gold paper with lots of cascading curlicue ribbons.

c. the one shaped like the camera you've been wanting.

Answers

5 or more a's
Mystery Maven:
It's no mystery that you love suspense, intrigue, and finding out secrets. You would probably really enjoy adventure or mystery stories.

5 or more b's
Flights of Fancy: You love to learn about magical people and places and to pretend you're lost in other worlds. Chances are, fantasy books would strike your fancy.

5 or more c's
Just the Facts, Ma'am: The truth is, you're intrigued by real-life situations and real people's problems. You should try reading nonfiction or realistic fiction.

A mix of a's, b's, and c's
Story Smorgasbord:
You have lots of different tastes and interests, so you could choose from a variety of different books—from fact to fiction!

Stress Test

Being involved can be a good thing, but being overcommitted can be a disaster! **Hook yourself up to the stress monitor** to see if your extracurricular schedule is balanced . . . or off the charts!

1. When you first wake up in the morning, you . . .

   a. wish you could stay in bed.

   b. worry that you don't have everything done.

   c. are excited and ready to start the day.

2. Lately, you find yourself getting annoyed with your friends and family . . .

   a. all the time.

   b. once in a while.

   c. almost never.

3. You have something scheduled after school . . .

   a. every day.

   b. most days.

   c. once in a while.

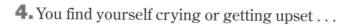

4. You find yourself crying or getting upset . . .

    a. every couple of days.

    b. every couple of weeks.

    c. hardly ever.

5. It's hard for you to find time to do things like clean your room, paint your nails, or read a book . . .

    a. often.

    b. sometimes.

    c. almost never.

6. You find yourself wishing there were more hours in the day . . .

    a. all the time.

    b. once a week.

    c. once a month.

7. You wake up in the night worrying . . .

    a. a couple times a week.

    b. a few times a month.

    c. hardly ever.

8. On the weekends, you have time to sleep in, hang out with your family, or do something just for you . . .

   a. once a month.

   b. every couple of weeks.

   c. every weekend.

Scoring

Give yourself 3 points for each a, 2 points for each b, and 1 point for each c.

19 to 24: Stress Mess:
You have so much going on in your life right now that it's time for a time-out. Take a moment and think about what's really important to you. Something *has* to go!

14 to 18: Happily Challenged:
It's great to be busy. But remember that too much of a good thing can become a bad thing. Keep an eye on your schedule and make sure you don't overdo it.

8 to 13: Stressless:
You're pretty comfortable with your schedule. You might take time to try out new activities that interest you. But don't feel like you have to be busy to be happy.

Best Buds?

Did you know that when you give someone a bouquet,
you're really sending a secret message? **Test your flower power**
by matching these blooms with their meanings.

_____ **1.** chrysanthemum

_____ **2.** buttercup

_____ **3.** mistletoe

_____ **4.** tulip

_____ **5.** lilac

_____ **6.** dandelion

_____ **7.** sunflower

_____ **8.** baby's breath

_____ **9.** orchid

_____ **10.** red rose

_____ **11.** sweet pea

a. You're so sweet.

b. See you later!

c. I promise.

d. You're a wonderful friend.

e. You're silly.

f. I believe in you.

g. You're beautiful.

h. Give me a smooch!

i. I love you.

j. You're famous!

k. Great job!

Answers

1. **d.** You're a wonderful friend. **2.** **e.** You're silly. **3.** **h.** Give me a smooch! **4.** **j.** You're famous!

5. **f.** I believe in you. **6.** **c.** I promise. **7.** **k.** Great job! **8.** **a.** You're so sweet.

9. **g.** You're beautiful. **10.** **i.** I love you. **11.** **b.** See you later!

Scoring

0 to 3 correct
Nipped in the Bud

Don't worry if you didn't know these. Now that you've learned how to send secret messages with flowers, have fun!

4 to 7 correct
Just Blossoming

You knew a lot of these! To learn even more, look for a book at your library!

8 to 11 correct
Blooming Genius

Nice going! You have true petal power.

Try sending messages to your friends using drawings of some of these flowers as codes.

What's Your Recipe for Making Friends?

When it comes to **making new friends,** do you bubble over with enthusiasm, or are you a bit slow to warm up?

1. You're vacationing at a beach cottage. Next door are two girls about your age. You . . .

a. run over and invite them to go swimming with you.

b. watch them for a while to see if they look nice before introducing yourself.

c. read your magazine outside and hope they see you and say hi.

2. A new girl has just started at your school. You . . .

a. ask her to sit with you at lunch.

b. smile when she sits next to you and tell her your name.

c. avoid her until you find out what she's like.

3. Your best pal, Beth, invites you to come to her house for a sleepover with her cousins. You . . .

a. can't wait to go. If the cousins are anything like Beth, you know you'll have a great time.

b. ask her a little bit about the cousins before deciding if you'll go.

c. tell her you're busy that night—you just know you'd feel weird spending the night with a bunch of girls you've never met.

4. Your family just moved, and you're going to your first day at the new school. The bus pulls up to your stop. You . . .

a. hop on and walk straight to the back, where all the action is.

b. cautiously find a seat in the middle with a girl who looks about your age.

c. sit in the first available seat—right behind the bus driver.

5. You're sitting in the bleachers at your brother's soccer game. Two girls are sitting next to you. You . . .

a. say, "Who wants to go get a hot dog?" to see if they'll join you.

b. ask them who they're there to watch.

c. listen in on their conversation to figure out if they're nice.

6. You're browsing through your favorite store at the mall while your mom is trying on shoes. The girl flipping through the rack next to you looks familiar. You . . .

a. say hi and ask if you know her.

b. smile and see if she smiles back.

c. keep shopping and see if she notices you.

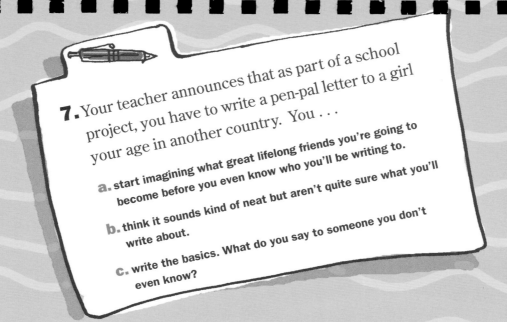

7. Your teacher announces that as part of a school project, you have to write a pen-pal letter to a girl your age in another country. You . . .

a. start imagining what great lifelong friends you're going to become before you even know who you'll be writing to.

b. think it sounds kind of neat but aren't quite sure what you'll write about.

c. write the basics. What do you say to someone you don't even know?

Scoring

Give yourself 1 point for each **c,** 2 points for each **b,** and 3 points for each **a.**

7 to 11

Slow Cooker: You tend to make friends slowly, which can make for strong and steady friendships. But be sure you're not letting great friendships slip through the cracks. All relationships involve a little risk—don't be afraid to take one if it means meeting a new pal.

12 to 16

Simmering: You're open to new people but are also cautious. Once you feel comfortable, you're not afraid to take the initiative to meet new friends or to let people get to know you.

17 to 21

Hot! Hot! Hot!: You're totally comfortable in new environments. With you and friends, the more the merrier! Make sure, though, that you're taking the time to nurture and grow the friendships you have.

Birds of a Feather

If you were a bird, what kind would you be? Choose the answers that describe you best and find out which **feathered friend** fits you.

1. When you get older, you would love a job as . . .

   a. Princess Odette in *Swan Lake* with the national tour of a ballet company.

   b. the *Quiz Book* editor.

   c. a Peace Corps volunteer teaching children in another country.

   d. a cover model for *American Woman* magazine.

   e. the star of a hilarious new television series.

   f. an award-winning roving photojournalist.

2. Your perfect day would be . . .

   a. shopping for antiques with your older sisters.

   b. sleeping till after noon and staying up half the night reading a novel.

   c. playing board games with your family in front of the fireplace.

   d. shopping for new clothes at the mega-mall.

   e. painting your bedroom fuschia and lime.

   f. hunting for seashells on the beach.

3. Your favorite shirt, blouse, or sweater is . . .

   a. elegant and lacy.

   b. dark and serious.

   c. soft and comfortable.

   d. decorated with glitter and rhinestones.

   e. bright and colorful.

   f. plain and simple.

4. On your dream vacation, you would most want to stay . . .

   a. at a beautiful country inn with fluffy canopy beds.

   b. right in the middle of a big city, within walking distance of museums and a huge art gallery.

   c. at your family's lake cottage—where you can relax on the dock.

   d. at a posh resort with poolside waiters, spa service, and a concierge to plan your day.

   e. on a tropical island—basking in the warm sun and frolicking in the soft white sand.

   f. at a campground in the wild west, horseback riding by day, and roasting marshmallows and singing around a campfire by night.

5. You most love to shop at . . .

   a. La Boutique, an expensive designer shop.

   b. A-Million-&-One Books bookstore.

   c. Hometowne Mall, where you can find everything you want under one roof.

   d. Glamour Girls jewelry and accessories store.

   e. The Buck $top dollar shop, where you can find lots of cool cheap stuff.

   f. Good Sports sporting goods store.

6. The scent that you like the most is . . .

   a. a bundle of freshly picked lilacs.

   b. a brand-new book, especially if it's the newest release from your favorite author.

   c. Dad's delicioso dinner cooking.

   d. your freshly shampooed hair.

   e. Mom's brand-new car.

   f. the air outside after a spring rain shower.

Answers

Mostly a's: You're like a swan and love graceful, elegant things.

Mostly b's: Like the wise owl, you are a night person and love knowledge.

Mostly c's: You're kind and caring and resemble the dove, the symbol of peace.

Mostly d's: Like the peacock, you adore making a big splash.

Mostly e's: Quirky and bright, you resemble the parrot.

Mostly f's: Like the eagle, you love freedom and to soar in the great outdoors!

Grudge Meter

When you feel that you've been wronged, do you
hold a grudge or can you **forgive and forget?**

1. Last year Alana didn't invite you to her birthday party. You're making up the guest list for your birthday bash, and you . . .

a. put her on the list since she's still part of your group.

b. put her down with a question mark since you're not sure what to do.

c. definitely do not invite her. If you weren't welcome at her party, she's not coming to yours.

2. Mrs. Harris, the school librarian, scolded you last year for talking in the library. Now, you . . .

a. show her how you've matured by smiling and zipping your lips whenever you see her.

b. avoid the library at all costs—or try to go during Mrs. Harris's lunch period.

c. call Mrs. Harris "Mrs. Scare-us" (behind her back, of course).

3. When you were little, your Uncle Mel used to call you Chubby Cheeks. Whenever you see him now, you . . .

a. smile and tell him about your last basketball game. You're not Chubby Cheeks anymore!

b. try to be polite. You still remember what he used to say, but you know he was just trying to be funny.

c. roll your eyes and leave the room. You have nothing to say to him.

4. Katelyn borrowed your favorite gel pen last week and lost it. She bought you a new one, but it's not the same as the one you had. You . . .

a. tell her it's O.K. A gel pen is a gel pen. It's not like she meant to lose it.

b. say "thanks," but make the decision to keep the lending to a minimum for a while.

c. find yourself thinking about it every time you use the pen, and end up treating Katelyn differently afterward.

5. At your softball game, you and Mariah collide as you both try to make the game-winning catch, and the ball drops to the ground between you. You have another game the next day. You . . .

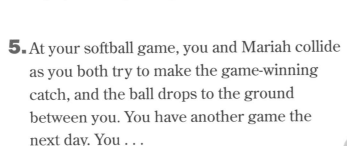

a. try to concentrate on getting ready for the game. What happened was yesterday's news.

b. talk to Mariah about you both remembering to yell "I got it!" before making a catch.

c. avoid Mariah, vow not to throw the ball to her, and whisper to your friends that you think she's a show-off.

6. The last time you painted your little sister's toenails, she accidentally spilled the bottle of nail polish all over your bedroom floor. Now she wants you to paint her nails again. You . . .

a. go ahead and do it. She didn't mean to make a mess the last time.

b. remember to put down newspaper this time and remind her to be careful.

c. tell her "No way!" You don't want her making another mess in your room.

7. Your kitten claws your favorite teddy bear to shreds. You . . .

   a. sigh and clean up the mess. He's just a kitten and you love him.

   b. put your other valuables away, then go on the Internet and get some information on kitten training.

   c. yell "Get outta here!" every time he comes into your room.

8. While cleaning out your closet, you find a mean note from Jennie to Chelsea about you that you intercepted last year. You . . .

   a. toss it without reading it again. You're all friends now, so who cares?

   b. try to think about what the fight was really about, then write in your journal about your newfound insights.

   c. save it, and don't speak to Jennie the next day at school.

Scoring

Score 1 point for each **a,** 2 points for each **b,** and 3 points for each **c.**

8 to 12:	13 to 18:	19 to 24:
Easy Come, Easy Go	**Future Focused**	**Grudge Master**
You let go of problems easily and leave the past behind you. Just be careful not to let people take advantage of your good nature.	You're pretty good at forgiving and forgetting, but you also want to prevent bad situations from happening again. You realize that you can't change the past, so you try to look to the future.	You have the memory of an elephant, but you can't let go of the times when you've been hurt. Ask yourself: *Did these people mean to hurt me?* Most of the time, the answer is no. When you hold a grudge, you're really hurting yourself. You'll feel better if you can let go of some of the anger you're holding.

The Scoop

Did you know that some people say your **favorite ice cream flavor** shows a lot about your personality? Circle your favorite flavor, then turn the page to see what it says about you.

Vanilla

Chocolate Chip

Double Chocolate Chunk

Strawberries and Cream

Banana Split

Butter Pecan

Answers

Vanilla: You're not just plain vanilla. You are always busy and have lots of friends. You expect an awful lot from yourself, though, so remember that it's O.K. to stop and taste the ice cream once in a while.

Strawberries and Cream: You're a bit on the shy side but comfortable exploring the world on your own. You like friends who look on the bright side of things.

Banana Split: You're easy to get along with and a good listener. You take most things in stride and don't let the little things get you down.

Chocolate Chip: You are always looking to the future, and wow, do you have great plans for yourself! You love to compete but aren't so happy when you lose.

Butter Pecan: You have your life all planned and organized. You tend to keep your feelings to yourself and go it alone.

Double Chocolate Chunk: You love to have fun and adore being the center of attention. You tend to trust other people and are always looking for friends. You follow your hunches.

Mighty Manners?

There's more to manners than "please" and "thank you."
See if you know what to do in these situations.

1. You call Allie to invite her over for dinner, but no one answers. Instead, you get her family's answering machine. You . . .

   a. hang up. You hate those machines.

   b. say, "Phone tag. You're it! Call me!" She'll know it's you.

   c. leave a message: "This is Jamie. Can Allie please call me back this afternoon?"

2. Mom is psyched to serve her new soup recipe when proper Aunt Emily comes over for dinner. You smile politely as you lift your soup spoon, then impress the adults by remembering to . . .

   a. daintily scoop the soup toward yourself (that's the proper way to eat soup, you know).

   b. blow lightly on each spoonful before you eat it.

   c. tilt your bowl to spoon up the last scrumptious drop!

3. Sweet peas are your favorite green veggie. But those babies can be hard to catch! To eat them, you should . . .

a. push a few peas onto your fork with your finger when nobody's looking.

b. carefully use your knife to corral the peas onto your fork.

c. quickly stab the peas with your fork.

4. After the group belts out the final notes of "Happy Birthday" at your friend's party, it's the moment you've been waiting for . . . the cake. But—wait—is that CARROT cake? Gross! Now what?

a. Take a small slice and give it a try. Maybe at least the frosting is yummy.

b. Announce to the group that you don't do veggies in your desserts, "No, thank you!"

c. Politely ask your friend's mom for a different kind of cake.

5. Oops! You drop your napkin way under the table at a restaurant and can't even reach it with your foot. You should . . .

a. crawl under the table and get it.

b. use your brother's.

c. ask for a new one.

6. Your friend Jensen sends you an e-mail loaded with details about an argument she had with another friend, Bethany. She doesn't say it's a secret, so you . . .

a. forward the message to a few other friends. Everyone has been having trouble with Bethany lately—this is so typical!

b. respond to Jensen but try to change the subject. Who knows where the message might end up?

c. respond to Jensen, but include Bethany in the reply (so that she gets a copy of Jensen's original message). She can't change unless she knows there's a problem.

7. Your stomach is growling and your usual dinnertime was an hour ago, but there's no sign of food yet at the party you're at. You . . .

a. look around and ask loudly, "So, when ARE we eating?"

b. sneak out to the kitchen and try to sneak a snack.

c. ask your friend to ask her mom for a little something to tide you over.

8. After your soccer game, the team heads to the Pizza Pit for the all-you-can-eat buffet. You're so hungry, you're ready for seconds before anyone else. When you go back to the buffet for another slice, you . . .

a. bring your plate with you. The dishwasher will appreciate having fewer dishes to wash.

b. leave your plate at the table. Just walk up to the buffet and get a slice—it's finger food!

c. start with a clean plate each time you return to the buffet. Who wants to use a dirty dish?

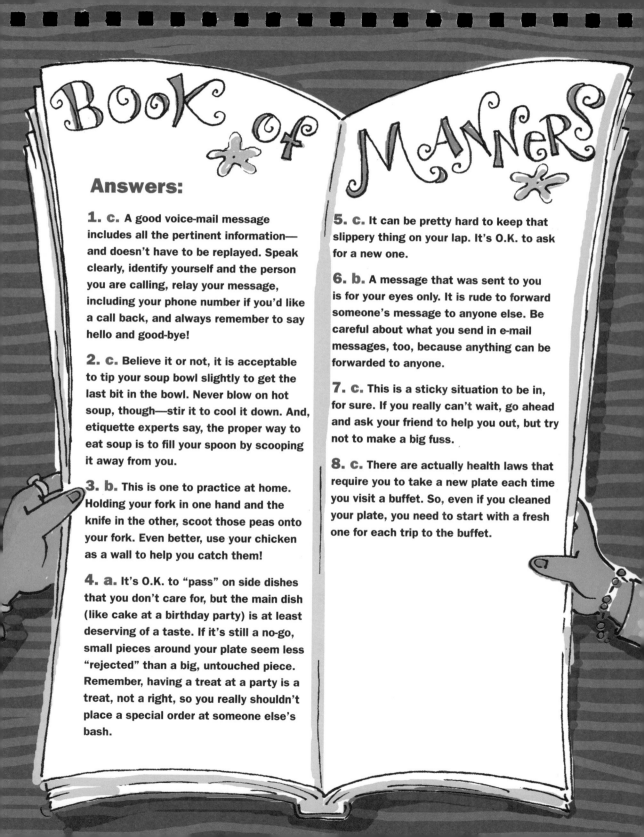

BOOK of MANNERS

Answers:

1. c. A good voice-mail message includes all the pertinent information—and doesn't have to be replayed. Speak clearly, identify yourself and the person you are calling, relay your message, including your phone number if you'd like a call back, and always remember to say hello and good-bye!

2. c. Believe it or not, it is acceptable to tip your soup bowl slightly to get the last bit in the bowl. Never blow on hot soup, though—stir it to cool it down. And, etiquette experts say, the proper way to eat soup is to fill your spoon by scooping it away from you.

3. b. This is one to practice at home. Holding your fork in one hand and the knife in the other, scoot those peas onto your fork. Even better, use your chicken as a wall to help you catch them!

4. a. It's O.K. to "pass" on side dishes that you don't care for, but the main dish (like cake at a birthday party) is at least deserving of a taste. If it's still a no-go, small pieces around your plate seem less "rejected" than a big, untouched piece. Remember, having a treat at a party is a treat, not a right, so you really shouldn't place a special order at someone else's bash.

5. c. It can be pretty hard to keep that slippery thing on your lap. It's O.K. to ask for a new one.

6. b. A message that was sent to you is for your eyes only. It is rude to forward someone's message to anyone else. Be careful about what you send in e-mail messages, too, because anything can be forwarded to anyone.

7. c. This is a sticky situation to be in, for sure. If you really can't wait, go ahead and ask your friend to help you out, but try not to make a big fuss.

8. c. There are actually health laws that require you to take a new plate each time you visit a buffet. So, even if you cleaned your plate, you need to start with a fresh one for each trip to the buffet.

Happy Birthstone!

Do you **know your birthstone?** How about your best friend's? For each month, write in the traditional birthstone from the list below. Then turn the page to see what each stone means.

Months

January *Garnet*

February *Amethyst*

March *Aquamarine*

April *diamond*

May *emerald*

June *perl*

July *ruby*

August *peridot*

September *sapphire*

October *opal*

November *topaz*

December *Turqoise*

Birthstones

 **Ruby**

 **Opal**

Turquoise

 **Topaz**

 **Peridot**

Emerald

 **Diamond**

 **Garnet**

 **Amethyst**

 **Pearl**

Aquamarine

 Sapphire

Answers

The meanings of birthstones trace back to stories, beliefs, and legends—some more than a thousand years old! Are they for real? Who knows? Read the answers and see what you think.

January
Garnet

The garnet symbolizes confidence, grace, and loyalty, and is thought to encourage friendships. Some believe wearing a garnet helps protect you from harm.

February
Amethyst

The amethyst symbolizes love, sincerity, and honesty. Legend says that wearing an amethyst can help calm your fears and keep you from excessiveness. Others believe an amethyst under your pillow brings pleasant dreams!

March
Aquamarine

"Aquamarine" is Latin for "sea water," so it's a perfect stone for anyone who loves the ocean. Some believe wearing an aquamarine could bring love and affection.

April
Diamond

The hardest stone, the diamond signifies purity, strength, and love. The diamond is considered the ultimate gift of love and is the most common stone in engagement rings.

May
Emerald

The emerald symbolizes spring, hope, and peace. If you looked at an emerald under a microscope, you would see tiny patterns that look like plants in a garden.

June
Pearl

Pearls represent innocence, health, and wealth. Pearls can also stand for wisdom or something precious. A pearl starts out as a tiny particle of sand in an oyster shell. Some pearls take up to three years to get large enough to be used in jewelry!

July
Ruby

The ruby represents kindness, happiness, and honor. In ancient times, people believed that rubies helped cure illnesses and patch up arguments.

August
Peridot

The peridot symbolizes fame, honor, and protection. Legends say pirates loved peridots. It was thought that wearing a peridot set in gold would prevent bad dreams and bring friendship, success, and good luck.

September
Sapphire

Sapphires stand for wisdom, truth, and sincerity. When you wear a sapphire, some say you might feel secure, brave, and strong.

October
Opal

Opals are a symbol of hope, confidence, and innocence. More than 500 years ago, during the Middle Ages, young blonde girls in Europe wore opals in their hair to protect its beautiful color. A good opal has the colors of all the other birthstones in it.

November
Topaz

Topaz represents friendship, faithfulness, and honesty. Some people believe wearing a topaz could bring friendship, fame, and fortune!

December
Turquoise

Turquoise symbolizes happiness, good health, good luck, and success. Giving or receiving a turquoise as a gift is like a pledge of friendship!

Are You an All-American Girl?

Take this quiz and see how much you know about **the good old U.S.A.!**

1. It's right before kickoff at your brother's football game. Everyone stands to sing the national anthem. What song is it?

   a. "America the Beautiful"

   b. "The Star-Spangled Banner"

   c. "Take Me Out to the Ball Game"

   d. "My Country 'Tis of Thee"

2. It's your job to draw the American flag for your group social studies project. For extra credit, you need to write a brief explanation of your work. Quick—what do the 13 stripes on the flag stand for?

   a. the 13th president of the United States

   b. the 13 original colonies

   c. the original 13 flavors of ice cream

   d. the number of signatures on the Declaration of Independence

3. Your gym teacher says you'll be practicing the "great American pastime" in your next gym class. What game are you getting pumped to play?

   a. baseball

   b. football

   c. soccer

   d. kickball

4. Your birthday card from Grandma arrived. She always includes a crisp $10 bill. Whose portrait are you expecting to find on the cash inside?

a. Alexander Hamilton

b. Thomas Jefferson

c. Ronald Reagan

d. George Washington

5. Your best friend lives in New York and you live in California. You have to tell her about what happened in school today, but you don't want to call too late. When it's 9 P.M. in California, what time is it in New York?

a. 9 P.M. What is this, a trick question?

b. 6 P.M. She's probably just sitting down to dinner.

c. Midnight. You'd better wait until tomorrow to call.

d. 11 P.M. It's two hours later there . . . but that's still too late to call.

6. Your mom won the sales award at work, and her company gave her and Dad a trip to what is known as "The Youngest State." Where are they going? (Hint: It was the last state to enter the Union.)

a. Alaska

b. Hawaii

c. Puerto Rico

d. Florida

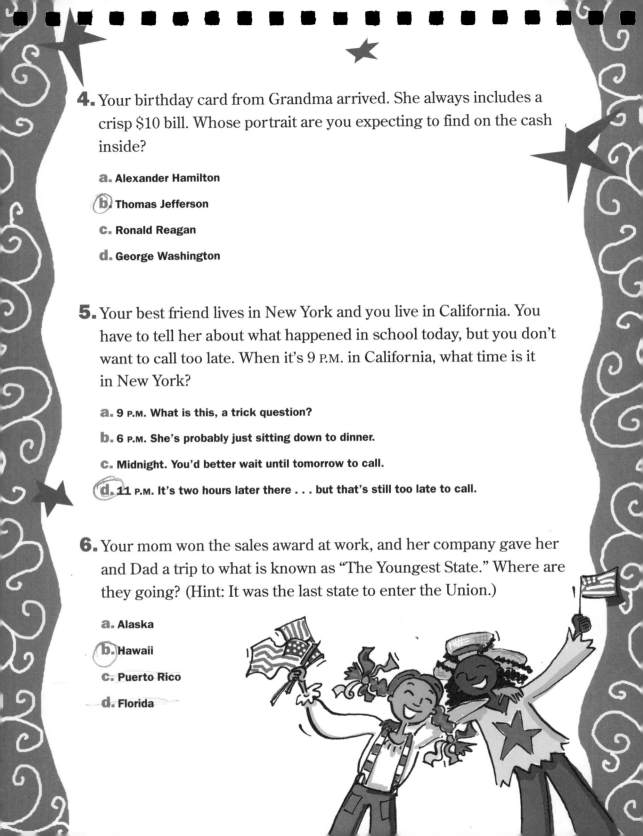

7. During summer break, your family is driving to South Dakota to see Mount Rushmore. What famous face do you NOT expect to see carved in stone?

a. George Washington

b. John F. Kennedy

c. Thomas Jefferson

d. Theodore Roosevelt

8. You signed up to help with the scenery for the school Thanksgiving play. You're in charge of painting the pilgrims' ship. What ship or ships brought pilgrims to America?

a. the *Susan Constant*

b. the *Mayflower*

c. the *Titanic*

d. the *Nina*, the *Pinta*, and the *Santa Maria*

9. Your mom adores Thai food and your dad loves Italian. But you prefer American fare. Which of these American foods was not actually invented in America? (HINT: More than one answer is correct!)

a. ice cream

b. hot dog

c. apple pie

d. French fries

e. pizza

f. bagels

Answers: 1. b **2.** b **3.** a **4.** a **5.** a **6.** b **7.** b (Abraham Lincoln is the fourth face.) **8.** b **9. None** of them were actually invented in America . . . **a.** France **b.** Germany **c.** England **d.** Belgium **e.** Italy **f.** Germany

Send us your quiz ideas!

Have an idea for an awesome original quiz?
Got something you really want to know about yourself?

Tell us your best ideas for quizzes.
We just might . . .

a. make another Quiz Book.
b. have fun reading your answers.
c. publish your quiz on our Web site.

Write to us at:
Quiz Book Editor
Pleasant Company Publications
P.O. Box 620998, 8400 Fairway Place
Middleton, WI 53562

Or visit our Web site at
www.americangirl.com.

Published by Pleasant Company Publications
Copyright © 2003 by American Girl, LLC

Questions or comments? Call 1-800-845-0005, or write
American Girl, P.O. Box 620497, Middleton, WI 53562-0497.

Visit our Web site at **americangirl.com**

Printed in China.
05 06 07 08 09 10 LEO 13 12 11 10 9

American Girl® and American Girl Library® are registered trademarks of American Girl, LLC.

Editorial Development: Julie Williams, Michelle Watkins, and Sara Hunt

Art Direction and Design: Chris Lorette David

Consultant: Patricia K. Criswell, ACSW

Production: Kendra Pulvermacher, Mindy Rappe, Judith Lary, and Jeannette Bailey

Quiz on pp.68–69 based on information courtesy of Alan R. Hirsch, M.D.,
from his book *What Flavor Is Your Personality* (Naperville, IL: Sourcebooks, Inc., 2001).